# BENSON
# Handwriting
## WITH READING AND LANGUAGE ARTS

**3**

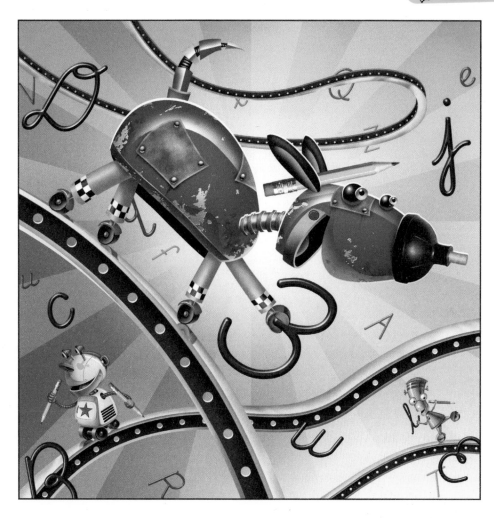

**Perfection Learning®**

**Editorial Director:** Susan C. Thies
**Design Director:** Randy Messer
**Lead Designer:** Emily J. Adickes
**Illustrators:** Sue F. Cornelison, Mike Aspengren

**Reviewers:**

Anita Craig
Kindergarten teacher
Academic Center
Prairie Hills School District
Markham, IL

Lauren Donelson
Intervention teacher
PS7 Elementary School
St. Hope Public School District
Sacramento, CA

Janie Ephland
Literacy coach
Fort Worth Independent School District
Fort Worth, TX

Kay Iandoli
First-grade teacher
Ginnings Elementary
Denton Independent School District
Denton, TX

Amanda Jones
Third-grade teacher
Mt. Vernon Elementary School
Mt. Vernon Independent School District
Mt. Vernon, TX

Shelli Miller
First-grade teacher
Cessna Elementary School
Wichita Public School District
Wichita, KS

Sebria Mitchell
Second-grade teacher
Jackson Elementary School
Tyler Independent School District
Tyler, TX

Linnea Patrick
Third-grade teacher
Brunson Elementary School
Winston-Salem/Forsyth County School District
Winston-Salem, NC

Mariana Salazar
Second-grade bilingual teacher
Club Hill Elementary School
Garland Independent School District
Garland, TX

Cheryl Thrasher
Third-grade teacher
Everett Elementary
North Lamar Independent School District
Paris, TX

Jennifer Willden
Third-grade teacher
Hugh Gallagher Elementary School
Storey County School District
Virginia City, NV

# Contents

## On a Roll with Uppercase Letters

## Showing What You've Learned

# Writers on a Roll

# Are You Left-Handed or Right-Handed?

**If you write with your left hand:**

Sit tall in your chair with both of your feet flat on the floor. Slant your paper so that it is up on the left and down on the right. Hold it with your right hand.

Hold your pencil with your first two fingers and your thumb. Keep your left arm close to your body. When you write, pull your pencil toward your left elbow.

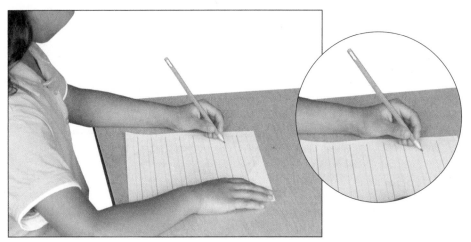

**If you write with your right hand:**

Sit tall in your chair with both of your feet flat on the floor. Slant your paper so that it is up on the right and down on the left. Hold it with your left hand.

Hold your pencil with your first two fingers and your thumb. Keep your right arm close to your body. When you write, pull your pencil toward your right elbow.

# Keep the Focus: Strokes, Spacing, Size, and Slant

## Just Four Strokes

Just four simple strokes and you can write any letter or numeral.

Use a red crayon to trace the **vertical** lines. Use a blue crayon to trace the **horizontal** lines. Use a pencil to trace the **circles**, both backward and forward. Then use a color of your choice to trace the **slanted** lines. They may slant right or left.

F  L  I  x  7  c  P  3

## Watch Your Space

Letters in words should not touch each other. Leave a space about the width of a pencil or paper clip between words.

Write Space Your Words below. Use your pencil or a paper clip to check the spacing.

## Size Matters

Letters and numerals come in three sizes—tall, small, and below the line. All letters sit on the baseline. Tall letters touch the skyline. Small letters touch the midline. Below-the-line letters touch the midline but hang below the baseline.

Write a word below with at least one of all three sizes of letters.

## Vertical

Manuscript letters are straight up and down. Pull straight down when you form your letters.

Trace the vertical lines in the letters below.

up and down

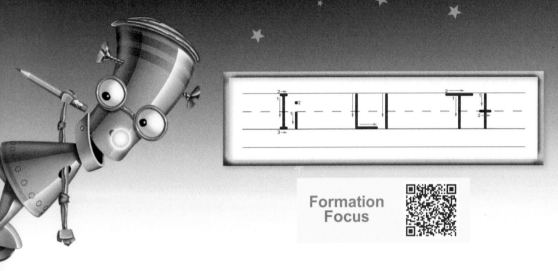

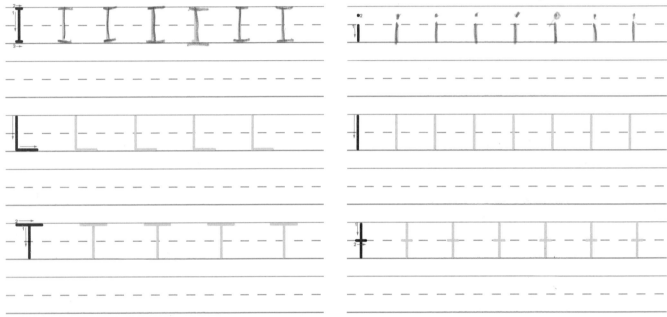

Iowa Idaho Illinois Tennessee

finally minutes building nothing

island material built syllables

**Formation Focus**

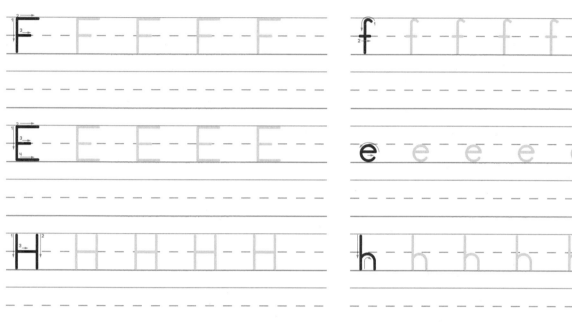

Hawaii Honolulu Florida

surface feel behind force

explain heat check heavy

## Oo Dd Cc

Formation Focus

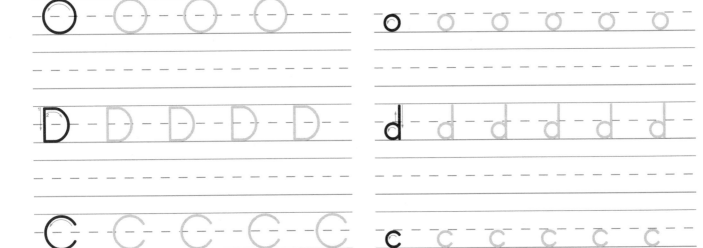

O O O O

o o o o o o

D D D D D

d d d d d d

C C C C C

c c c c c c

Oklahoma Oregon California

correct decided contain

ocean stood thousands

Formation Focus

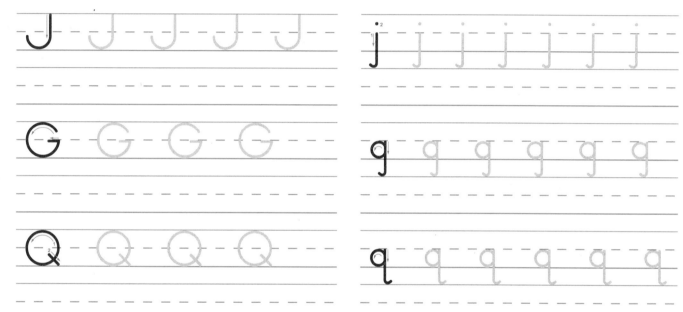

Georgia New Jersey Juneau

government general subject

length job edge glass region

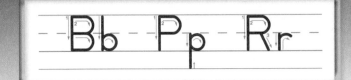

Bb Pp Rr

Formation
Focus

B B B B B       b b b b b b

P P P P P       p p p p p p

R R R R R       r r r r r r

Pennsylvania Rhode Island

perhaps probably brother

present paragraph represent

## Ss Uu Aa

Formation
Focus

S S S S S  s s s s s s

U U U U U  u u u u u u

A A A A A  a a a a a a

South Carolina Utah Arkansas

carefully square suddenly

beautiful instruments laughed

## Mm Nn Zz Kk

M M M M M    m m m m m

N N N N N    n n n n n

Z Z Z Z Z    z z z z z

K K K K K    k k k k k

Maryland Minnesota Nebraska

Kentucky millions months

quickly among skin bank

V V V V V

v v v v v v

W W W W W

w w w w w w

X X X X X

x x x x x x

Y Y Y Y Y

y y y y y y

Wisconsin Washington

New York wheels divided

yesterday exactly valley

# Time to Show Off

## Have You Ever Seen?

Have you ever seen a sheet on a riverbed?
Or a single hair from a hammer's head?
Has the foot of a mountain any toes?
And is there a pair of garden hose?
Are the teeth of a rake ever going to bite?
Have the hands of a clock any left or right?
Does the needle ever wink its eye?
Why doesn't the wing of a building fly?

## Have You Ever Seen?

Have you ever seen a sheet on a riverbed?
Or a single hair from a hammer's head?
Has the foot of a mountain any toes?
And is there a pair of garden hose?
Are the teeth of a rake ever going to bite?
Have the hands of a clock any left or right?
Does the needle ever wink its eye?
Why doesn't the wing of a building fly?

Write the poem in your best manuscript handwriting. At the end of this book, you'll be writing this poem in cursive!

# All of the Letters and Numerals

Look at the letters and numerals. Some of the cursive forms look very much like the manuscript letters. Others are quite a bit different.

Circle the cursive letters that you think look most like the manuscript forms. Underline the letter that you think is the most different in cursive.

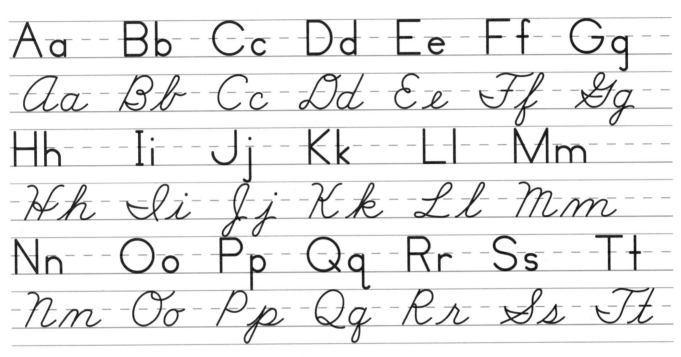

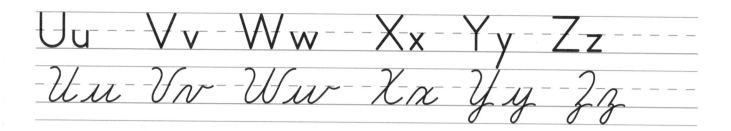

Uu  Vv  Ww  Xx  Yy  Zz

*Uu  Vv  Ww  Xx  Yy  Zz*

Circle the numeral or numerals in your birthday date.

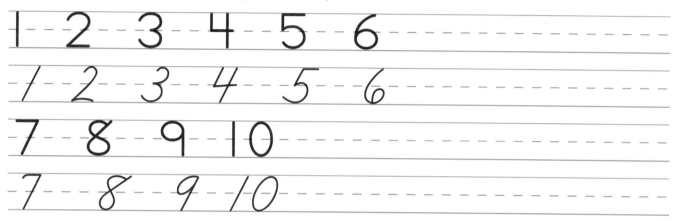

1  2  3  4  5  6

1  2  3  4  5  6

7  8  9  10

7  8  9  10

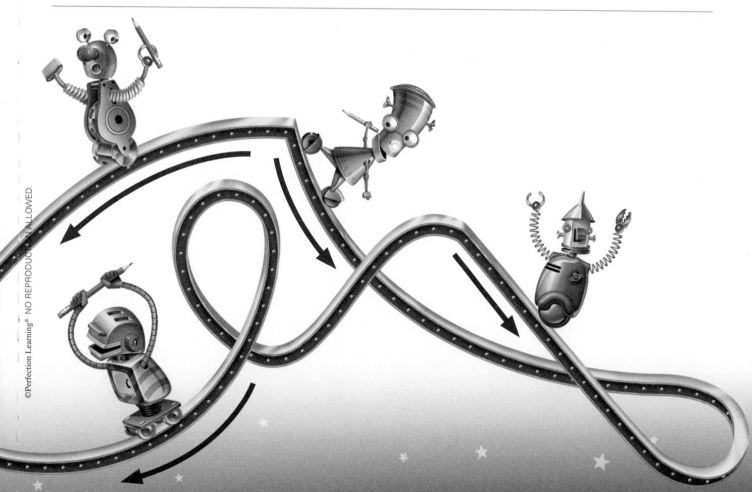

# Writing Left-Handed

## If you write with your left hand:

Sit in your chair with both of your feet flat
on the floor. Lean forward just a bit. Both
of your arms should bend at a 90° angle
to rest on your desk or table.

Slant your paper so that it is up on the left
and down on the right. Hold it with your
right hand. Use your right hand to shift
your paper as you write.

Hold your pencil with your first two fingers
and your thumb. Keep your first finger
on top of the pencil. Don't squeeze your
pencil too hard.

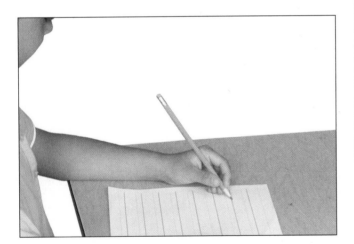

# Writing Right-Handed

## If you write with your right hand:

Sit in your chair with both of your feet flat on the floor. Lean forward just a bit. Both of your arms should bend at a 90° angle to rest on your desk or table.

Slant your paper so that it is up on the right and down on the left. Hold it with your left hand. Use your left hand to shift your paper as you write.

Hold your pencil with your first two fingers and your thumb. Keep your first finger on top of the pencil. Don't squeeze your pencil too hard.

# Recognizing Cursive

It may take you a little while to get used to reading cursive writing. Still, you are such a good reader by now, it won't be long before you're reading cursive easily.

Look at the cursive letters below. Write the matching manuscript letter. You can check pages 20–21 if you get stumped.

| | | | | | |
|---|---|---|---|---|---|
| *e* | | *c* | | *F* | |
| *m* | | *a* | | *V* | |
| *b* | | *y* | | *S* | |
| *j* | | *x* | | *B* | |
| *o* | | *i* | | *W* | |
| *t* | | *G* | | *K* | |
| *d* | | *L* | | *E* | |
| *k* | | *n* | | *T* | |
| *g* | | *p* | | *D* | |
| *z* | | *Q* | | *Y* | |

Read the math words below written in cursive. Write them in manuscript.

addition

subtraction

triangle

coins

fractions

hundreds

tens

ones

inch

foot

# Learning the Strokes
# Curve Under

**Curve under** is an important stroke that begins more than half of all lowercase cursive letters, as well as several uppercase letters.

For all lowercase cursive letters, this stroke begins on the baseline and extends to the midline or the skyline.

Trace and practice the **curve under** strokes that reach the midline.

Trace and practice the **curve under** strokes that reach the skyline.
For uppercase cursive letters, this stroke begins on the baseline or the midline and extends to the skyline. Trace the **curve under** strokes that begin on the baseline.

Trace and practice the **curve under** strokes that begin on the midline and reach the skyline.

Trace the **curve under** strokes that begin the letters below.

*i  e  u  w  r  s  y  p  j*

*l  t  b  h  k  f*

*L  S  G*

# Learning the Strokes
## Curve Down

**Curve down** strokes are used in lowercase and uppercase cursive letters, as well as several numerals.

**Curve down** strokes begin at the midline for lowercase cursive letters.

Trace and practice the **curve down** strokes that begin at the midline.

**Curve down** strokes begin at the skyline for uppercase cursive letters.
Trace and practice the curve down strokes that begin at the skyline.

Trace the **curve down** strokes that begin the letters and numerals below.

# Learning the Strokes
## Curve Over

**Curve over** strokes begin many uppercase cursive letters and only a few lowercase cursive letters.

**Curve over** strokes begin at the baseline and extend to the midline for lowercase cursive letters.

Trace and practice the **curve over** strokes that begin at the baseline and reach the midline.

**Curve over** strokes begin at the skyline for most uppercase cursive letters. A few of these letters have short **curve over** strokes that begin at the skyline but quickly extend into another stroke.

Trace and practice the **curve over** strokes that begin at the skyline and slant down to the baseline.

The three uppercase cursive letters below have **curve over** strokes that begin on the baseline and extend to the skyline.

Trace the beginning **curve over** strokes that start on the baseline in the letters below.

Trace the beginning **curve over** strokes that start at the skyline in the uppercase letters below.

# Learning the Strokes
## Slant **and Loop**

**Slant strokes** begin three uppercase cursive letters and two numerals. Beginning slant strokes all start at the skyline.

While **slant strokes** don't begin many cursive letters, they are used at least once in nearly every lowercase and uppercase cursive letter. This makes the **slant stroke** very important.

Trace and practice the beginning **slant strokes** that start at the skyline.

Trace and practice the **slant strokes** that begin at the midline.

**Loop strokes** don't begin any cursive letters, but they are part of the formation of many lowercase and uppercase cursive letters. These strokes can loop back or forward.

**Loop back strokes** can reach from the skyline to the baseline.
Trace and practice the curve under and loop back strokes below.

Several lowercase and uppercase cursive letters have **loop back** or **loop forward strokes** that are below the baseline. Trace and practice the letters below with loop back and loop forward strokes below the baseline.

## Keep the Focus
# Spacing, Size, and Slant

**Spacing**
Even though cursive letters are joined, spacing between letters is still important. If your cursive letters aren't spaced, the words will be difficult to read.

*These letters are too close together.*

*These letters are spaced properly.*

**Size**
Just as with manuscript letters, cursive letters can be tall, small, and below the line. As you learn cursive, keep your tall letters tall so they touch the skyline and sit on the baseline.

*l  t  b  S  m  a  I*

Keep your small letters small, between the midline and the baseline.

*s  m  e  u  w*

Keep your below-the-line letters at the midline or, in some cases, the skyline but below the baseline.

*j  g  p  q  z  f*

**Slant**
Cursive letter have a forward slant. As you learn to form cursive letters and then words, you'll want to focus on keeping your letters all slanting to the same degree.

*As you learn cursive, write*

*letters with a forward slant.*

# Curve Under

More than half of the lowercase cursive letters begin with the curve under stroke. The curve under stroke always begins on the baseline.

For all of these lowercase letters, the **curve under** stroke begins on the baseline and extends to the midline.

*i  e  u  w  r  s  y  p  j*

Practice curve under strokes.

For all of these lowercase letters, the curve under stroke begins on the baseline and extends to the skyline.

*t  l  b  h  k  f*

Practice curve under strokes.

1. Curve under, slant down, curve under to join.
2. Dot.

**Formation Focus**

*hi up high*

Trace and write.

 *i    i    i    i    i    i    i    i    i    i*

Cursive letters are joined to form words.
Join *i* and *i*. Notice that the last stroke on the *i* is a curve under to join.

*ii    ii    ii    iii    iii    iii*

*i*

## CURSIVE TIP

Cursive handwriting flows because the letters are joined. Most of the time, your pencil should not leave the paper until you finish a word. When you form *i*, the second step is to add the dot. In cursive, you wait until the word is finished. Then you go back and add the dot.

1. Curve under, slant down, curve under to join.
2. Slide right across.

**Formation Focus**

*a toad being towed*

Trace and write.

*t   t   t   t   t   t   t   t   t   t   t   t*

Practice joining *t* and *i*. Notice that both *t* and *i* end with the curve under to join.

*ti   ti   ti   ti   ti   ti*

*it   it   it   it   it   it*

*t*

## CURSIVE TIP

Remember, cursive handwriting is joined and should flow. When you form *t*, the second step is to cross the letter at the midline. In cursive, you wait until the word is finished. Then you go back and add the cross.

Curve under, loop back, slant down.
Curve under to join.

**Formation Focus**

*sealing the ceiling*

Trace and write.

*e e e e e e e e e e e e*

Practice joining *e* and other letters. Notice that *e* ends with the curve under to join.

*ee ei ie te et*

*iet tie tie tee tee*

**Keep the Focus** **Spacing** Are your curve under joining strokes the right size to keep your letters evenly spaced?

35

Curve under, slant down.
Curve under, slant down.
Curve under to join.

**Formation Focus**

*unicorn in a uniform*

Trace and write.

*u  u  u  u  u  u  u  u  u*

Practice joining *u* and other letters. The letters you have learned all have curve under to curve under joinings.

*uu  uu  ut  ut  ui  ue*

*tui  tiu  ute  iut  tuu*

*u*

○ **Keep the Focus** **Slant** Are your cursive letters all slanted to the same degree?

36

Curve under, slant down.
Curve under, slant down.
Curve under, sidestroke right.

**Formation Focus**

*wailing whale*

Trace and write.

*w*    *w*    *w*    *w*    *w*    *w*    *w*

Practice joining *w* and other letters you have learned. The joining stroke in *w* is a sidestroke. Notice how the *w* joins to other letters at the midline.

*we    wi    wu    tw    uw*

*wit    wet    tie    tiw    wee*

○ **Keep the Focus**    **Strokes** Does your *w* end with a sidestroke right joining stroke?

**37**

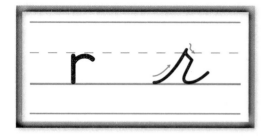

Curve under, slant down right.
Slant down, curve under to join.

**Formation Focus**

*rows of roses*

Trace and write.

r r r r r r r r r r

Practice joining *r* and other letters you have learned. This letter ends with a curve under to join.

*rw rr rt ri re ru*

*row rit rut ruw write*

*r*

 **Keep the Focus** **Size** Do all of your cursive letters sit on the baseline?

**38**

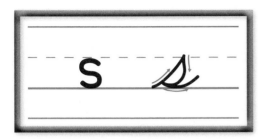

Curve under, curve forward and around.
Curve under to join.

**Formation Focus**

$5+5=$

$\begin{array}{r} 17 \\ + \ 5 \\ \hline \end{array}$

$\begin{array}{r} 38 \\ + 61 \\ \hline \end{array}$

*some silly sums*

Trace and write.

*s s s s s s s s s s s s s*

Practice joining *s* and other letters you have learned. This letter ends with a curve under to join.

*sw se si st ss su*

*sit sew suw see stew*

*s*

**Keep the Focus** **Size** Does your *s* touch the midline?

39

©Perfection Learning® NO REPRODUCTION ALLOWED.

Curve under, loop back, slant down, curve under to join.

**Formation Focus**

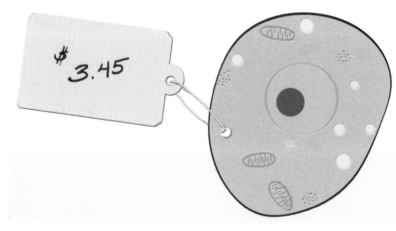

$3.45

*a cell to sell*

Trace and write.

*l   l   l   l   l   l   l   l   l   l   l   l   l   l*

Practice joining *l* with other letters you have learned. This is the first tall letter you have practiced with the loop back stroke. As with most of the letters you've learned, this letter ends with the curve under to join.

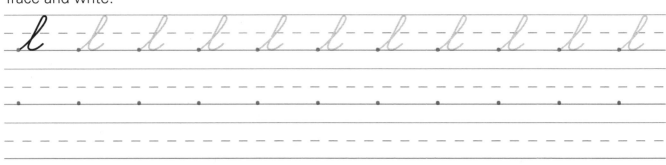

*ll    lt    lw    lu    lr    ls*

*lui    let    rll    slit    rule*

*l*

 **Keep the Focus**    **Size** Do all of your tall cursive letters touch the skyline?

Curve under, loop back, slant down, curve under. Sidestroke right.

**Formation Focus**

*a bare bear*

Trace and write.

*b b b b b b b b b*

Practice joining *b* and other letters you have learned. This letter joins with a sidestroke right at the midline. What other letter have you learned that joins this way?

*be bw wb bt bi br*

*bet bus bite web blue*

 **Keep the Focus**  **Strokes** Notice how the last sidestroke right to join has to dip down when the following letter is an *e*.

h *h*

Curve under, loop back, slant down.
Trace up, curve over, slant down.
Curve under to join.

**Formation Focus**

*a hoarse horse*

Trace and write.

*h h h h h h h h h h*

Practice joining *h* and other letters you have learned.

*hi hb hr wh he sh*

*hit hut hill hub her*

Keep the Focus  **Spacing** Are your words spaced so they can be easily read?

42

Curve under, loop back, slant down.
Trace up, curve over and back, slant down.
Curve under to join.

**Formation Focus**

*a knock-kneed knight*

Trace and write.

*k    k    k    k    k    k    k    k    k*

Practice joining *k* and other letters you have learned.

*ke    ki    ks    wk    bk    kt*

*kit    kew    tike    klb    luk*

*k*

○ **Keep the Focus**   **Size** Do your curve over and back strokes fit between the midline and the baseline?

Curve under, slant down.
Curve under, slant down, loop back.
Curve over to join.

**Formation Focus**

*yo-yo yard sale*

Trace and write.

*y    y    y    y    y    y    y    y    y    y*

Practice joining *y* and other letters you have learned. This letter ends with a curve over to join. Notice how the curve over becomes a curve under to join and start the next letter.

*ye    yt    yi    yr    ys    yy*

*yet    yes    bye    buy    yikes*

*y*

**○ Keep the Focus** **Size** Does your below-the-line loop back stroke sit on the blue line below the baseline?

Curve under, loop back, slant down,
loop forward and up.
Curve under to join.

**Formation Focus**

*flowers in the flour*

Trace and write.

Practice joining *f* to other letters you have learned. Notice that this letter goes below the baseline and loops forward up to the baseline.

fe    fi    ft    fu    fs    fl

fit    fur    fib    fuss    flew

 **Keep the Focus**    **Size** Make sure your cursive *f* touches the skyline as well as the blue line below the baseline.

Curve under, slant down.
Loop back, trace up, curve over.
Trace and curve under to join.

**Formation Focus**

*a pair of pears*

Trace and write.

*p p p p p p p p p p p*

Practice joining *p* to other letters you have learned. Notice that this letter goes below the baseline and loops back up to the midline.

*pe pw pl pr pi pu*

*pet pie type lip purr*

**Keep the Focus**  **Slant** Are all of your letters leaning to the right?

1. Curve under, slant down, loop back. Curve over to join.
2. Dot.

**Formation Focus**

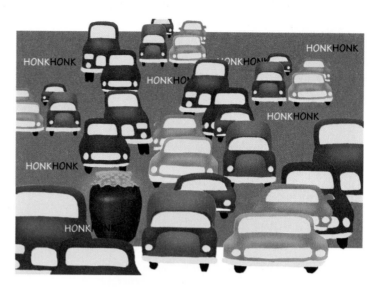

*jam in a jam*

Trace and write.

*j  j  j  j  j  j  j  j  j  j  j  j  j*

Practice joining *j* to other letters you have learned. This letter ends with a curve over to join. Notice how the curve over becomes a curve under to join and start the next letter. What other letter have you learned with the same joining stroke?

*jl  jr  ji  ju  jp  jf*

*jut  jet  jury  just  luj*

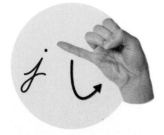

### CURSIVE TIP

When you form *j*, the second step is to add the dot. In cursive, you wait until the word is finished. Then you go back and add the dot.

# Time for Review

You have learned to write 15 lowercase cursive letters that all begin with the curve under stroke.

Use the words in the word box and find an antonym for each word below. Write the antonym on the line next to the word. Then write a rhyming word for the antonym.

| sit | full | bye |
|-----|------|------|
| fib | fly | hilly |
| buy | few | her |

|  | **Antonym** | **Rhyming Word** |
|------|------|------|
| many | | |
| land | | |
| stand | | |
| truth | | |
| empty | | |
| him | | |
| flat | | |
| sell | | |
| hello | | |

# Joinings: Curve Under

All lowercase cursive letters are joined. Most of the joinings you have been practicing with your new letters are curve under to curve under. Use these letters and write as many words as you can. They will all be curve under to curve under joinings.

*i t u e l h f k r s p*

# Keep the Focus: Strokes

Using the five basic strokes, you'll be able to write all the cursive lowercase and uppercase letters.

Curve under

Curve down

Curve over

Slant

Loop

Write the name of the stroke that begins each letter below.

*i* _____ *a*

*s* _____ *n*

*d* _____ *u*

Circle the letters below with a loop stroke.

*c   z   w   k   m*

Circle the letters below with a slant stroke.

*n   d   w   t   y*

# Curve Down

Curve down strokes begin at the midline for lowercase cursive letters. These letters begin with the curve down stroke.

*a  d  o  c  g  q*

Practice curve down strokes.

Remembering good writing position and pencil grip will help you with cursive handwriting. Whether you are left-handed or right-handed, make sure that you are sitting comfortably in your chair or seat with your feet flat on the floor.

**Left-handed writers**

**Right-handed writers**

Hold your pencil with your first two fingers and your thumb. Keep your first finger on top of the pencil. Keep your fingers relaxed. Try not to squeeze the pencil too hard.

Curve down, slant up, trace, slant down.
Curve under to join.

**Formation Focus**

*the ants' aunt*

Trace and write.

*a a a a a a a a a a a a a a*

Practice joining *a* to other letters you have learned. If *a* is not the first letter, notice how you have to curve under and up to the midline to begin the curve down stroke of the *a*.

*as at ar au ap ab*

*ate teak lay ask last*

**Keep the Focus**    **Strokes** Did your curve down stroke begin just below the midline?

52

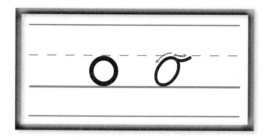

Curve down and around.
Sidestroke right.

**Formation Focus**

*a goat eating coats*

Trace and write.

*o o o o o o o o o o o o o o*

Practice joining *o* to other letters you have learned. This letter ends with a sidestroke to join. Joining with a sidestroke means you slide over and begin the next letter near the midline.

*or oh os of oo op*

*oat coat tote toss boys*

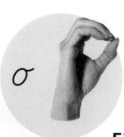

○ **Keep the Focus** **Strokes** Does your *o* sidestroke right to join?

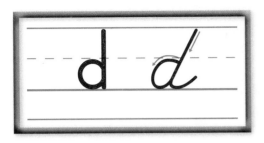

Curve down, slant up, trace down.
Curve under to join.

**Formation Focus**

*a deer's dear*

Trace and write.

$d$ $d$ $d$ $d$ $d$ $d$ $d$ $d$ $d$ $d$ $d$ $d$

Practice joining $d$ to other letters you have learned.

*do    dt    dr    du    da    dh*

*dad    dear    deer    dress    sled*

*d*

○ **Keep the Focus**   **Spacing** Are your joining strokes the right size to keep the letters spaced in your words?

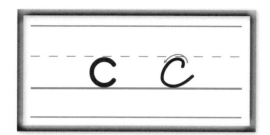

Curve down, curve under to join.

*clothes that close*

Trace and write.

c  c  c  c  c  c  c  c  c  c  c  c  c  c

Practice joining *c* to other letters you have learned.

*ca    co    ch    cr    cl    ce*

*cat   cup   act   clue   crust*

 **Keep the Focus** **Strokes** Does your *c* begin just below the midline but touch the midline as it curves down?

g g

Curve down, slant up.
Trace, slant down, loop back.
Curve over to join.

**Formation Focus**

*a goose with goose bumps*

Trace and write.

g g g g g g g g g g g g g

Practice joining *g* to other letters you have learned. This letter ends with a curve over to join.
Remember that the curve over becomes a curve under to join and start the next letter.

*gl gr gi gl gu gw*

*guy goose tag beg huge*

*g*

 **Keep the Focus**     **Size** Does your *g* touch the blue line below the baseline?

Curve down, slant up, trace,
slant down, loop forward and up.
Curve under to join.

**Formation
Focus**

*a cracked quack*

Trace and write.

q q q q q q q q q q q q q q q q

Practice joining *q* to other letters you have learned. Remember to loop forward below the baseline and then curve under to join.

qu qu qu qu qu qu

qui quick quack quiet

○ **Keep the
Focus**   **Strokes** Does your *q* curve under to join?

# Time for Review

You have already learned to write 21 lowercase cursive letters! All the letters you've learned begin with the curve under or curve down stroke.

---

Syllables: Remember that a syllable is a part of a word. Each syllable must have a vowel sound.

*teach* + *er* = *teacher*
base word    suffix

*re* + *teach* = *reteach*
prefix    base word

*black* + *bird* = *blackbird*
word    word    compound word

---

Read the words below. How many syllables do you hear? Write the words in the correct category.

*rewrite*    *syllables*    *keep*    *laugh*

*surprises*    *lake*    *hopeless*    *pushed*

*schoolhouse*    *likeable*    *electric*    *serious*

*clothes*    *quickest*    *careful*

| One Syllable | Two Syllables | Three or More Syllables |
| --- | --- | --- |
| | | |

# Joinings: Curve Under, Curve Down

All lowercase cursive letters are joined. You have just learned the lowercase letters that begin with the curve down stroke. Write the words below in ABC order to practice joining curve under and curve down letters.

*tag*
*shoot*
*cup*
*at*
*right*
*help*

*quiet*
*drag*
*shop*
*quack*
*flight*
*chalk*

*path*
*great*
*practice*
*golf*
*delight*
*watch*

left-handers

# Keep the Focus: Spacing

Even though lowercase cursive letters within a word are all joined, spacing is still important. If the letters are too close, handwriting is difficult to read. Study the examples below. Make sure your joining strokes swing wide enough that your letters are spaced and not touching.

*close    wide    right*

Keep your words spaced so your readers can easily see where one word ends and another begins.

*tooclose    too    wide*

*just right*

Practice word and letter spacing below.

*right*

*just right*

# Curve Over

Curve over strokes that start lowercase cursive letters begin at the baseline. These letters begin with the curve over stroke.

Practice curve over strokes.

The curve over stroke is also used in other lowercase letters that begin with a different stroke.

Circle the curve over stroke in the following letters. Then practice writing the letters on the line below.

The curve over stroke is also a joining stroke in some lowercase letters.

Circle the curve over joining stroke in the following letters. Then practice writing the letters on the line below.

Curve over, slant down.
Trace up, curve over, slant down.
Curve under to join.

**Formation Focus**

*a knight at night*

Trace and write.

*n  m  m  m  m  m  m  m  m*

Practice joining *n* to other letters you have learned.

*na  no  nu  ne  ni  nn*

*nag  tan  sun  wren  band*

*n*

○ **Keep the Focus**    **Strokes** Do both of your curve over strokes touch the midline?

62

Curve over, slant down.
Trace up, curve over, slant down.
Trace up, curve over, slant down.
Curve under to join.

**Formation Focus**

How do you do?

*meet the meat*

Trace and write.

*m    m    m    m    m    m    m*

Practice joining *m* to other letters you have learned. This letter joins with a curve under stroke.

*ma    mu    me    mi    mo*

*mat    meet    meat    ham*

*m*

 **Keep the Focus**    **Strokes** Do all three of your curve over strokes touch the midline?

Curve over and down, curve under, sidestroke right.

**Formation Focus**

*vowels in a verb*

Trace and write.

*n   n   n   n   n   n   n   n   n*

Practice joining *n* to other letters you have learned. This letter joins with a sidestroke. What other letters have you learned that join with a sidestroke right?

*nu   na   ne   ni   ni   nr*

*net   nat   have   verb   vowels*

○ **Keep the Focus**    **Strokes** Does your *n* end with a sidestroke right to join?

1. Curve over, slant down right. Curve under to join.
2. Slant down left.

**Formation Focus**

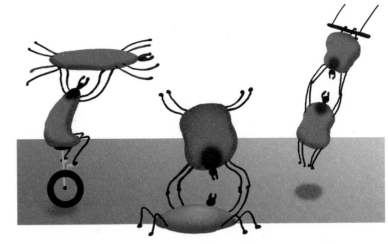

*six ticks doing tricks*

Trace and write.

*x  x  x  x  x  x  x  x  x*

Practice joining *x* to other letters you have learned.

*ox   ax   ex   xx   ux   xt*

*box   six   taxes   flax   fox*

### CURSIVE TIP

Cursive handwriting flows because the letters are joined. Most of the time, your pencil should not leave the paper until you finish a word. When you form *x*, the second step is to add the cross by slanting down left to the baseline. In cursive, you wait until the word is finished. Then you go back and add the slant stroke.

Curve over, slant down.
Trace, curve over, slant down.
Loop back and up, curve over to join.

**Formation Focus**

*when bees freeze*

Trace and write.

Practice joining *z* to other letters you have learned. This letter ends with the curve over to join.
Remember that the curve over becomes a curve under to join and start the next letter.

*zo   za   zi   ze   zz   zu*

*zip   zoom   buzz   freeze*

**Keep the Focus**   **Strokes** Check to make sure your first slant down stroke touches the midline.

# Joinings:
# Curve Under, Curve Over, Curve Down

All lowercase letters are joined. Since you have now learned all the lowercase letters, you are ready for all the different combinations of joinings. Practice curve under, curve over, and curve down joinings by matching the group names and their members and writing them below.

## Group Names

deck     herd
army     litter
flock     set
team
crowd

## Members

birds     people
ants     athletes
cards     buffalo
kittens
dishes

## Group Names

## Members

# Joinings:
# Sidestroke

A few lowercase letters end with the sidestroke for joining. The sidestroke may have to join with a curve under, a curve over, or a curve down. Practice these joinings using the words below. Read the words. Then write them in the correct category.

| | | | | |
|---|---|---|---|---|
| baboon | bake | bedbug | beige | bend |
| better | bicycle | build | bitter | bookcase |
| borrow | boxer | oatmeal | observe | occur |
| octopus | odor | old | wide | very |
| wade | wag | wait | water | weak |
| weird | white | | | |

| Nouns | Verbs | Adjectives |
|---|---|---|

# Time to Show Off

Now that you know all 26 lowercase cursive letters, it's time to show off.

Write the letters below in cursive.

m  n  z  v  x

a  o  d  c  g  q

i  t  e  u  w

r  s  l  b  h

k  y  f  p  j

Write the science words below in cursive.

fossil

liquid

weather

mixture

recycle

mammal

insect

oxygen

matter

solid

# Keep the Focus: Size

All of the uppercase cursive letters touch the skyline. Still, the other guidelines are also important when you write uppercase letters.

Look at the uppercase letters below. They use the midline as a guide in their formation.

These uppercase cursive letters touch the skyline, but they extend below the baseline and use it as an important guideline.

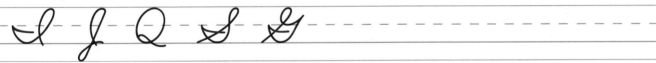

Even though all uppercase cursive letters touch the skyline, they begin on different guidelines. Many uppercase cursive letters begin at the skyline.

Some uppercase cursive letters begin at the baseline.

And one uppercase cursive letter even begins at the midline.

So even though all uppercase cursive letters touch the skyline, all of the guidelines are important as you learn to write these letters!

# Curve Down

The first five uppercase cursive letters you will be learning begin with the curve down stroke. For uppercase letters, the curve down stroke always begins at the skyline.

Use a crayon to trace the curve down stroke in these uppercase cursive letters.

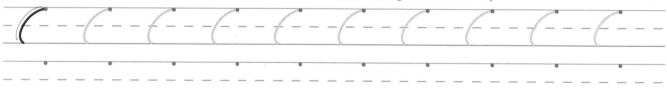

Trace and write to practice the curve down stroke that begins at the skyline.

## Uppercase Cursive Letters and Joinings

You have learned that all lowercase cursive letters are joined. You have also learned and practiced many different joinings.

Not all uppercase cursive letters are joined. It depends on their ending stroke. Three of these letters end with the curve under stroke at the baseline and join to the letters that follow.

However, the two uppercase cursive letters below end with a curve under stroke at the skyline and do not join to following letters.

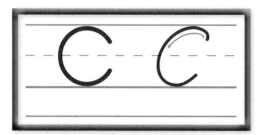

Curve down, curve under to join.

California

Trace and write.

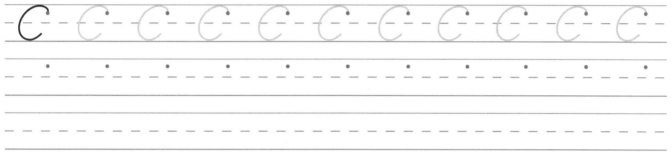

Practice joining $C$ to other letters you have learned. This letter ends with the curve under to join.

*Chandra   China   Coolidge*

*Crescent City, California*

*Chandra visited California.*

 **Keep the Focus**   **Slant** Make sure your uppercase cursive $C$ slants to the right.

**Formation
Focus**

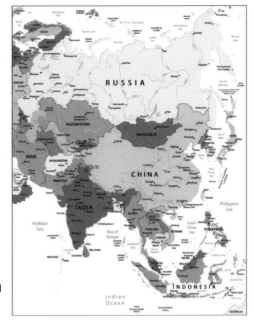

Asia

Curve down, curve under, trace, slant down.
Curve under to join.

Trace and write.

𝒶 𝒶 𝒶 𝒶 𝒶 𝒶 𝒶 𝒶 𝒶 𝒶

Practice joining 𝒶 to other letters you have learned. This letter ends with the curve under to join.

Anil Alabama Australia

Anchorage, Alaska

Asia is a continent.

 **Keep the Focus** **Spacing** Check your spacing between words.

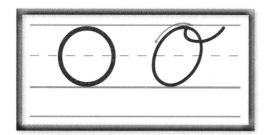

**Formation Focus**

Curve down, curve under and around, loop back, curve under.

October

Trace and write.

𝒪 𝒪 𝒪 𝒪 𝒪 𝒪 𝒪 𝒪 𝒪 𝒪 𝒪 𝒪

Write words that begin with uppercase 𝒪. The uppercase 𝒪 is not a joining letter.

*Oneisha October Oklahoma*

*Oregon City, Oregon*

*We buy pumpkins in October.*

 **Keep the Focus** — **Strokes** Remember that uppercase 𝒪 is not a joining letter.

Curve down, loop back, curve down, curve under to join.

**Formation Focus**

Earth

Trace and write.

Practice joining 𝓔 to other letters you have learned. This letter ends with the curve under to join.

*Eduardo Egypt England*

*Europe is a continent.*

*Earth is a planet.*

**Keep the Focus** **Strokes** Did you begin your 𝓔 just below the skyline?

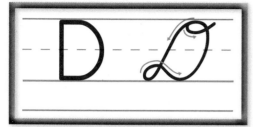

**Formation Focus**

Denmark

Curve down, loop back and around,
curve under. Loop back, curve under.

Trace and write.

$\mathcal{D}$ $\mathcal{D}$ $\mathcal{D}$ $\mathcal{D}$ $\mathcal{D}$ $\mathcal{D}$ $\mathcal{D}$ $\mathcal{D}$ $\mathcal{D}$ $\mathcal{D}$

Write words that begin with uppercase $\mathcal{D}$. The uppercase $\mathcal{D}$ is not a joining letter.

*Daeshawn    December*

*Copenhagen, Denmark*

*Devin is from Denmark.*

 **Keep the Focus** **Spacing** Even though uppercase $\mathcal{D}$ is not a joining letter, remember to keep it close to the next letter in the word.

# Time for Review

Write the book titles in the correct category below.

All About Denmark

Danny and the Dinosaur

Olive's Ocean

Ancient Egypt

Cade's Calico Cat

Europe

China

Alberto's Aunt

## Fiction

## Nonfiction

# Curve Over

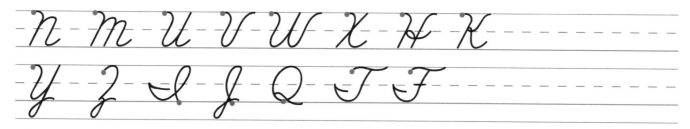

All of the above uppercase cursive letters begin with the curve over stroke. For uppercase cursive letters, the curve over stroke usually begins at the skyline.

However, for the following three letters, the curve over stroke begins on the baseline.

Use a crayon to trace the curve over stroke in these uppercase cursive letters. The curve over stroke begins at the skyline for these letters.

Trace and write to practice the curve over stroke that begins at the skyline.

Trace and write to practice the curve over stroke that begins at the baseline.

## Uppercase Cursive Letters and Joinings

As you have already learned, not all uppercase cursive letters are joined. It depends on their ending stroke. These letters that begin with the curve over stroke do not end with joining strokes.

Nadia Plants a Tree on Arbor Day

Curve over, slant down, trace up.
Curve over, slant down, curve under to join.

Trace and write.

*n n n n n n n n n n n n*

Practice joining *n* to other letters you have learned. This letter ends with the curve under to join.

*Nadia November Nashville*

*Nebraska City, Nebraska*

*Nadia celebrated Arbor Day.*

 **Keep the Focus** **Size** Notice that the second curve over stroke does not touch the skyline.

**Formation Focus**

Mammoth Cave

Curve over, slant down, trace up.
Curve over, slant down, trace up.
Curve over, slant down, curve under to join.

Trace and write.

$m$  $m$  $m$  $m$  $m$  $m$  $m$  $m$  $m$

Practice joining $m$ to other letters you have learned. This letter ends with the curve under to join.

*Mayah   March   Monday*

*Mammoth Cave*

*Maria saw Mammoth Cave.*

 **Keep the Focus**   **Size** Make sure that the last curve over stroke is lower than the previous one.

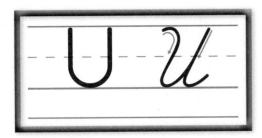

Curve over, slant down, curve under.
Trace, slant down, curve under to join.

Uganda

Trace and write.

𝒰 𝒰 𝒰 𝒰 𝒰 𝒰 𝒰 𝒰 𝒰 𝒰 𝒰

Practice joining 𝒰 to other letters you have learned. This letter ends with the curve under to join.

*Ulysses Uganda Ukraine*

*Cedar City, Utah*

*Uganda is in Africa.*

 **Keep the
Focus**   **Size** Does your uppercase 𝒰 touch the skyline twice?

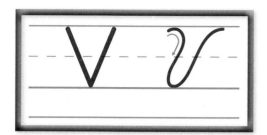

**Formation Focus**

Curve over, slant down, curve under, curve over.

Valentine's Day

Trace and write.

Write words that begin with uppercase *V*. The uppercase *V* is not a joining letter. Notice that the end stroke for *V* is a curve over at the skyline.

*Vincent Virginia Vietnam*

*Valentine's Day Vermont*

*Valentine's Day is next month.*

©Perfection Learning® NO REPRODUCTION ALLOWED.

 **Keep the Focus** **Strokes** Does your uppercase V end with a curve over stroke that touches the skyline?

Formation Focus

Washington, D.C.

Curve over, slant down, curve under.
Trace, slant down, curve under, curve over.

Trace and write.

*W W W W W W W W W W*

Write words that begin with uppercase *W*. The uppercase *W* is not a joining letter.

*Waldo West Virginia*

*Washington, D. C.*

*That city is in Wood County.*

 **Keep the Focus** **Size** Does your uppercase *W* touch the skyline three times?

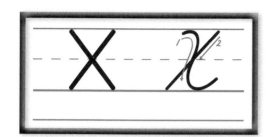

Xiao-Niao

1. Curve over, curve under to join.
2. Slant down left.

Trace and write.

𝒳   𝒳   𝒳   𝒳   𝒳   𝒳   𝒳   𝒳   𝒳   𝒳   𝒳

Write words that begin with uppercase 𝒳, which is a joining letter. The ending stroke for 𝒳 is a slant down left to the baseline, but the curve under stroke at the beginning joins with letters.

*Xander   Xiao-Niao*

*Xenia City, Colorado*

*Xiao-Niao is a Chinese name.*

## CURSIVE TIP

The uppercase cursive 𝒳 is a joining letter. The first stroke ends with a curve under to join. When you form 𝒳, the second step is to slant down left to the baseline. In cursive, you wait until the word is finished to add this second step.

Formation
Focus

Hawaii

1. Curve over, slant down.

2. Curve and slant down, trace up, loop back. Curve under to join.

right-handers

Trace and write.

Practice joining *H* to other letters you have learned. This letter ends with the curve under to join. This curve under is at the midline.

*Halim   Hartford   Helena*

*Honolulu, Hawaii*

*Halim vacationed in Hawaii.*

 **Keep the Focus**   **Slant** Make sure that both parts of your *H* are parallel as they slant to the right.

1. Curve over, slant down.
2. Curve over and slant down, loop forward, slant down. Curve under to join.

Kings Canyon
National Park

Trace and write.

𝒦  𝒦  𝒦  𝒦  𝒦  𝒦  𝒦  𝒦  𝒦  𝒦  𝒦

Practice joining 𝒦 to other letters you have learned. This letter ends with the curve under to join.

*Kadar   Kentucky   Korea*

*Kansas City, Kansas*

*Kings Canyon is in California.*

 **Keep the Focus**   **Strokes** Make sure your uppercase 𝒦 loops forward at the midline.

**Formation Focus**

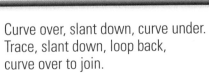

Curve over, slant down, curve under.
Trace, slant down, loop back,
curve over to join.

Yellowstone

Trace and write.

*Y Y Y Y Y Y Y Y Y Y Y*

Practice joining *Y* to other letters you have learned. This letter ends with the curve over stroke that becomes a curve under stroke to join to other letters.

*Yemena      Yellowstone*

*Yonkers, New York*

*Yellowstone is in three states.*

**Keep the Focus**   **Strokes** Does your uppercase *Y* end with a curve over to join?

88

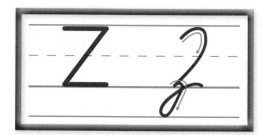

Zion National Park

Curve over, slant down, trace.
Curve over, slant down, loop back,
curve over to join.

Trace and write.

Practice joining $\mathscr{Z}$ to other letters you have learned. This letter ends with the curve over stroke that becomes a curve under stroke to join to other letters.

*Zachary    Zimbabwe*

*Zap, North Dakota*

*Zion is a park in Utah.*

**Keep the Focus**    **Strokes** Does your $\mathscr{Z}$ match the model?

Curve over, loop forward, curve under left,
sidestroke right.

Independence Day

Trace and write.

*I I I I I I I I I I I I*

Write words that begin with uppercase *I*. The uppercase *I* is not a joining letter.

*Indro   Illinois   India*

*Indianapolis, Indiana*

*We love Independence Day
fireworks.*

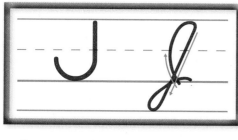

**Formation Focus**

Jupiter

Curve over, slant down, loop back.
Curve over to join.

Trace and write.

$\mathcal{J}$ $\mathcal{J}$ $\mathcal{J}$ $\mathcal{J}$ $\mathcal{J}$ $\mathcal{J}$ $\mathcal{J}$ $\mathcal{J}$ $\mathcal{J}$ $\mathcal{J}$ $\mathcal{J}$

Practice joining $\mathcal{J}$ to other letters you have learned. This letter ends with the curve over stroke that becomes a curve under stroke to join to other letters.

*Julio   January   Japan*

*Jefferson City, Missouri*

*Jupiter has many moons.*

 **Keep the Focus**   **Size** Does your $\mathcal{J}$ extend from the skyline to the blue line below the baseline?

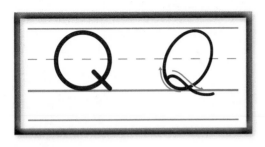

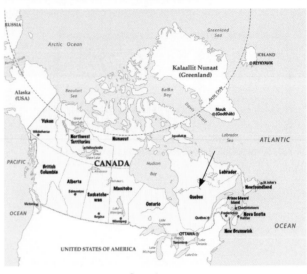

Quebec

Curve over and around, loop forward,
curve under.

Trace and write.

Q Q Q Q Q Q Q Q Q Q

Write words that begin with uppercase $Q$. The $Q$ is not a joining letter. Although in all English words, the letter $u$ follows $q$, that is not always true in words and names from other languages.

*Qing-Nian   Quito   Qatar*

*Quebec, Canada*

*Quebec is a province.*

 **Keep the Focus** **Strokes** Remember that $Q$ is not a joining letter, even though it ends with a curve under.

**Formation Focus**

Texas

1. Curve over, curve under.
2. Slant down, curve under left, sidestroke right.

Trace and write.

$\mathcal{T}$ $\mathcal{T}$ $\mathcal{T}$ $\mathcal{T}$ $\mathcal{T}$ $\mathcal{T}$ $\mathcal{T}$ $\mathcal{T}$ $\mathcal{T}$ $\mathcal{T}$ $\mathcal{T}$ $\mathcal{T}$ $\mathcal{T}$ $\mathcal{T}$

Write words that begin with uppercase $\mathcal{T}$. The uppercase $\mathcal{T}$ is not a joining letter.

*Tamako  Tuesday  Turkey*

*Texarkana, Texas*

*Texarkana is in two states.*

**Keep the Focus** **Strokes** After your pencil lift, make sure your slant down stroke begins in the middle of the first two strokes that form the top of the $\mathcal{T}$..

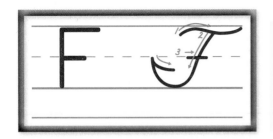

1. Curve over, curve under.
2. Slant down, curve under left, sidestroke right.
3. Slide right across.

Freedom Tower

Trace and write.

$\mathcal{F}$ $\mathcal{F}$ $\mathcal{F}$ $\mathcal{F}$ $\mathcal{F}$ $\mathcal{F}$ $\mathcal{F}$ $\mathcal{F}$ $\mathcal{F}$ $\mathcal{F}$ $\mathcal{F}$

Write words that begin with uppercase $\mathcal{F}$. The uppercase $\mathcal{F}$ is not a joining letter.

*Flores    Friday    France*

*Fort Myers, Florida*

*Where is the Freedom Tower?*

## CURSIVE TIP

The uppercase cursive $\mathcal{F}$ is not a joining letter. That means you don't have to wait until the end of the word to add the slide right across, or to cross the $\mathcal{F}$.

# Time for Review

Write the poem about the days of the week.

Monday's child is fair of face.
Tuesday's child is full of grace.
Wednesday's child is full of woe.
Thursday's child has far to go.
Friday's child is most forgiving.
Saturday's child works hard for her living.
Sunday's child is loving and giving.

# Curve Under and Slant Down

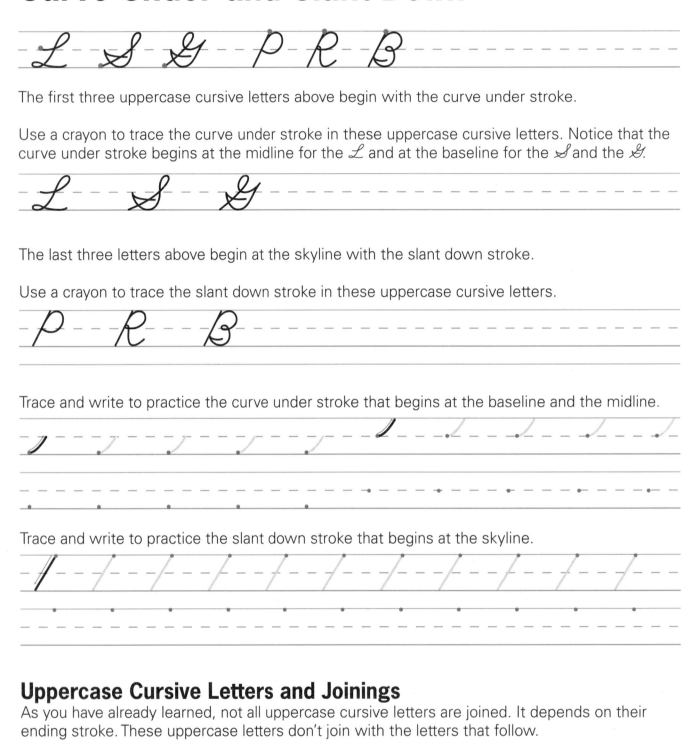

The first three uppercase cursive letters above begin with the curve under stroke.

Use a crayon to trace the curve under stroke in these uppercase cursive letters. Notice that the curve under stroke begins at the midline for the $\mathcal{L}$ and at the baseline for the $\mathcal{S}$ and the $\mathcal{G}$.

The last three letters above begin at the skyline with the slant down stroke.

Use a crayon to trace the slant down stroke in these uppercase cursive letters.

Trace and write to practice the curve under stroke that begins at the baseline and the midline.

Trace and write to practice the slant down stroke that begins at the skyline.

## Uppercase Cursive Letters and Joinings

As you have already learned, not all uppercase cursive letters are joined. It depends on their ending stroke. These uppercase letters don't join with the letters that follow.

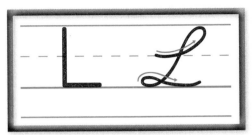

Louvre Museum

Curve under, loop back, slant down.
Curve over, sidestroke right to join.

Trace and write.

*L L L L L L L L L L*

Write words that begin with uppercase *L*. The *L* joins with a sidestroke right at the baseline.

*Lily Laos Lincoln*

*Lafayette, Louisiana*

*The Louvre is in France.*

**Keep the
Focus** **Strokes** Does your uppercase *L* begin on the midline?

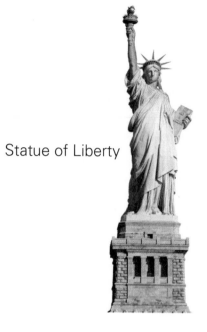

Statue of Liberty

Curve under, loop back, curve over.
Curve under, sidestroke right.

Trace and write.

Write words that begin with uppercase $\mathcal{S}$. The uppercase $\mathcal{S}$ is not a joining letter.

*Sasha    September    Saturday*

*Statue of Liberty*

*Sam was born in September.*

 **Keep the Focus**    **Size** Does your uppercase $\mathcal{S}$ look like the model?

Greece

Curve under, loop back, curve under.
Slant down, curve under left, sidestroke right.

Trace and write.

*G  G  G  G  G  G  G  G  G  G  G*

Write words that begin with uppercase *G*. The uppercase *G* is not a joining letter.

*Gabriella  Germany  Greece*

*Gainesville, Georgia*

*The first Olympics were in Greece.*

 **Keep the Focus**  **Spacing** Is your uppercase *G* close to the next letter in the word, even though it is not a joining letter?

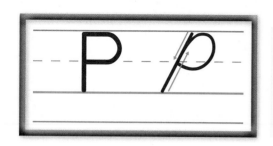

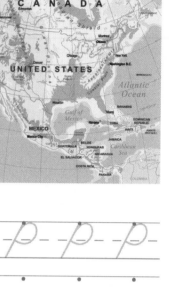

Pacific Ocean

Trace and write.

Write words that begin with uppercase P. The uppercase P is not a joining letter.

*Pedro Phoenix Paris*

*Pittsburgh, Pennsylvania*

*We swam in the Pacific Ocean.*

Mount Rushmore

Slant down, trace up, curve over and around.
Loop forward, slant down, curve under to join.

Trace and write.

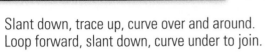

R  R  R  R  R  R  R  R  R  R  R

Write words that begin with uppercase *R*. The uppercase *R* joins with a curve under stroke.

*Raphael   Raleigh   Romania*

*Providence, Rhode Island*

*Have you seen Mount Rushmore?*

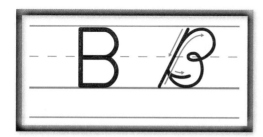

**Formation Focus**

Big Ben

Slant down, trace up, curve over and around.
Loop forward, curve over and around.
Sidestroke right.

Trace and write.

ℬ ℬ ℬ ℬ ℬ ℬ ℬ ℬ ℬ ℬ ℬ

Write words that begin with uppercase ℬ. The uppercase ℬ is not a joining letter.

*Belinda Brazil Britain*

*Boston, Massachusetts*

*Big Ben is in London.*

 **Keep the Focus** **Strokes** Does your loop forward stroke touch the midline?

# Time for Review

Read the following paragraph about Beverly Cleary. Then write the paragraph below.

Beverly Cleary is my favorite author. My teacher said that Beverly Cleary had trouble reading when she was first learning. I sometimes have trouble reading, but I still love it. I have read five of Beverly Cleary's books. I have read about Henry, Ribsy, Beezus, and Ramona. Ramona is my favorite character. I have a big sister who is bossy like Beezus, so I understand how Ramona feels. Ramona is funny. People tell me I'm funny too.

# Time to Show Off

Show what you have learned below. Write the uppercase letters in cursive.

A B C D E F G H I J K L M

N O P Q R S T U V W X Y Z

Now write these popular movie titles in cursive.

Babe

Peter Pan

Beauty and the Beast

Fly Away Home

The Lion King

Monsters, Inc.

Snow White

The Wizard of Oz

# Writing Cursive Numerals

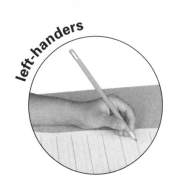

left-handers

Formation Focus  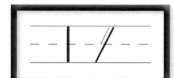    Slant down.

Formation Focus      Curve over, slant down, curve over.

Formation Focus      Curve over, trace, curve over.

Formation Focus  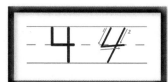    1. Slant down, slide right.   2. Slant down.

Formation Focus     Slide left, slant down, curve over.

**Keep the Focus**   **Strokes** Does your 4 slide right at the midline?

**105**

**Formation Focus**

Curve down, around, and over.

**Formation Focus**

Curve over, slide right, slant down.

**Formation Focus**

Curve down, curve over, slant up.

**Formation Focus**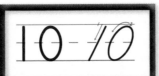

Curve down, slant up, slant down.

**Formation Focus**

1. Slant down.
2. Curve down and around.

**Keep the Focus** **Slant** Do your cursive numerals slant to the right like the models?

106

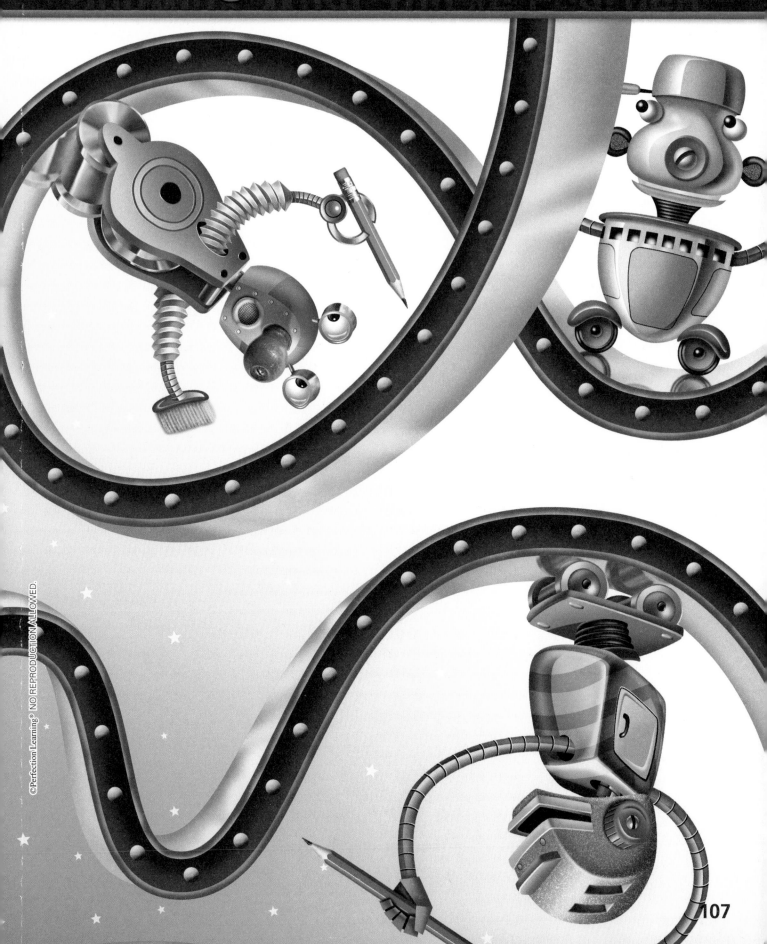

# Abbreviations

An **abbreviation** is a shortened form of a word or phrase. Abbreviations for states are the most commonly used abbreviations.

TX is the abbreviation for Texas.

*New York     South Dakota     Virginia     Minnesota*
*Hawaii     Washington     California     Ohio*
*Tennessee*

Write the state names below that match the abbreviations.

1. CA _____

2. HI _____

3. OH _____

4. MN _____

5. NY _____

6. SD _____

7. TN _____

8. VA _____

9. WA _____

# Writing a Summary

A **summary** is a shortened version of something. When you summarize a story, you tell just the most important parts.

Summarize the following fable in three sentences. Use your best cursive writing.

*At one time, Fox and Stork were good friends. Fox invited Stork to dinner. To be funny, she gave her guest soup in a shallow dish. Fox could easily lap up the soup. But Stork could only wet the end of his long bill. By the end of the meal, he was still hungry.*

*"I'm sorry you didn't enjoy your meal," said Fox with a grin.*

*"Don't worry about it," said Stork.*

*A few days later, Stork invited Fox to come to his house for dinner. He served the meal in a tall jar with a very narrow opening. Fox could not get her snout inside the jar. But Stork's long bill fit in just fine. This time it was Fox who went hungry.*

# Thank-You Note

A well-written thank-you note should
- State the gift or the act you are thanking someone for
- Mention your reason for being thankful
- Include a closing statement

Read the thank-you note below. Then use your best cursive to write it on the lines below.

Dear Aunt Rosa,

Thank you so much for inviting me to your apartment for the weekend. I enjoyed spending time with you and seeing where you work. Going out to eat and to the movie was a special treat. I can't wait to see you again when you visit for Christmas.

Love,
Maria

# Understanding Literary Text

**Literary text** is fiction text. Fiction is created in the imagination of the author. It is a made-up story.

Read the following paragraphs. Then answer the questions that follow. Write complete sentences and use your best cursive writing.

Paige sat on her bed and sighed. It was Saturday morning and she still hadn't thought of an idea for her science report. She only had until Monday to decide. It was going to be a long weekend.

Then Paige heard loud chirps outside her bedroom window. She hurried over to check the nest she had spotted days earlier. It had held three pale blue eggs. Now the nest was filled with three tiny birds. Their mouths were wide open, and they looked hungry. The mother bird was just landing on the edge of the nest with an insect in her beak. Paige watched for a while as the mother flew back and forth, bringing food to the little birds.

Then Paige had an idea. She grabbed her notebook and wrote "Science Report" in big letters on the first page.

1. What is Paige's problem?

_____

_____

2. How is Paige's problem solved?

_____

_____

# Understanding Informational Text

**Informational text** is a type of nonfiction writing. It is written to inform the reader.

Read the following paragraph about sound. Then answer the questions that follow. Write complete sentences and use your best cursive writing.

*Sound is made when objects vibrate, or move back and forth very quickly. These vibrations form sound waves that travel through the air to your outer ear. The sound waves move from your outer ear to your middle ear. There they go through a liquid and make tiny hairs move. The moving hairs send messages to your brain, where they are turned into sounds. This all happens so fast that you hear the sound at once!*

What is the meaning of the word *vibrate*?

_____

_____

_____

How is your brain involved in hearing sounds?

_____

_____

_____

_____

# Using Text Evidence

**Text evidence** is actual sentences from a text. When you answer a question about a text, you may be asked to use text evidence to support your answer.

Read the paragraph about thunderstorms. Then find and write the sentence from the paragraph that answers each question. Use your best cursive handwriting.

*Thunderstorms can bring damaging hail or flooding rains. These severe storms are caused by electricity that builds up in the clouds. When there is too much electricity, a spark jumps from cloud to cloud or from cloud to ground. The spark is called lightning. Lightning heats the air around it and makes the air explode. The explosion is what we call thunder.*

1. What causes thunderstorms?

2. How does lightning cause thunder?

# Poetry

Write the poem below. Use your best cursive handwriting.

The Caterpillar

Brown and furry
Caterpillar in a hurry,
Take your walk
To the shady leaf or stalk.
May no toad spy you,
May the little birds pass by you;
Spin and die,
To live again a butterfly.

*by Christina Rossetti*

# Writing Poetry

Write a biopoem. Follow the directions and finish the sentence starters to create your biopoem. Use your best cursive handwriting.

(First name)

_____

(Three adjectives)

Who is _____

(Two or three ideas)

Who loves _____

(Two or three ideas)

Who needs _____

(Two or three ideas)

Who enjoys _____

(Two or three ideas)

Who fears _____

(Person, place, or idea)

Who would like to see _____

(City, State)

Who is a resident of _____

# Friendly Letter

Use the form below to write a friendly letter. Consider some of the following ideas:

- Write a letter to a friend who has moved.
- Write a letter to a parent. Tell why you appreciate him or her.
- Write a letter to your grandparents. Tell about something that happened to you this week at home or at school.
- Write a letter to a friend not in your class. Explain something that happened today at recess or lunch.
- Write a letter to your teacher. Tell about something that happened to you during a vacation or over the weekend.
- Write a letter to an author. Explain a book you've read and why you liked it.
- Write a letter to your best friend explaining what a good friend he or she is.

Use your best cursive handwriting.

# Personal Narrative

A **personal narrative** is a story about yourself.

Write a story about how you have changed since you first started school in kindergarten. Use your best cursive writing.

# Informational Text

Read the facts about bats. Then write about bats using the facts and other facts you may know. Remember to organize the facts so that they make sense, and use complete sentences. Use your best cursive writing.

## Bats

1,000 different bat species
The only mammals that can fly
¼ of all the mammals on Earth are bats
Most eat insects
Some eat fruit or other mammals, birds, or lizards
Small brown bats can eat 1,000 mosquitoes in one hour
Smallest: one-inch body
Largest: six-foot wingspan
Life span: around thirty years
Shelter: caves, tree cavities, buildings
Migrate or hibernate in winter
May live alone or in colonies

# Procedural Text

**Procedural text** is a type of informational text that gives directions about how to do something. A recipe is procedural text.

Characteristics of Procedural Text:
- Explains how to do or make something
- May include a list of materials needed to make something
- Has numbered steps that tell what to do

Think of a game you like to play or a simple recipe you make and write directions on the next page. Use your best cursive handwriting.

## Building a Birdhouse

How do you build a birdhouse? It's easy.

 **Step 1:** Glue the four walls together.

**Step 2:** Glue the bottom onto the house.

 **Step 3:** Glue the roof pieces together.

 **Step 4:** Then glue the roof to the top of the house.

 **Step 5:** Once the glue is dry, you can paint your birdhouse.

# Fluency

Fluency in writing means that you can write quickly and neatly without thinking about each letter. With practice, writing fluently will become easier and easier. Practice writing fluently below.

Read the following sentence. It uses every letter in the alphabet. Then practice writing it below. Write it quickly and neatly.

*A mad boxer shot a quick, gloved jab to the jaw of his dizzy partner.*

Now write it again, a little faster this time.

Write the sentence two more times below. Try to write it faster each time.

Now look back at the sentences you wrote. Is the last one as easy to read as the first one? Were you able to write the sentence more quickly each time?

# Time to Show Off

Write the poem in your best cursive handwriting.

## Have You Ever Seen?

Have you ever seen a sheet on a riverbed?
Or a single hair from a hammer's head?
Has the foot of a mountain any toes?
And is there a pair of garden hose?
Are the teeth of a rake ever going to bite?
Have the hands of a clock any left or right?
Does the needle ever wink its eye?
Why doesn't the wing of a building fly?